MYTHS
IN 30 SECONDS

First published in the UK in 2013 by

Ivy Press

210 High Street

Lewes

East Sussex BN7 2NS

United Kingdom

www.ivypress.co.uk

ISBN: 978-1-908005-74-8

This book was conceived, designed and produced by

Ivy Press

CREATIVE DIRECTOR   Peter Bridgewater

MANAGING EDITOR   Hazel Songhurst

PROJECT EDITOR   Cath Senker

ART DIRECTOR   Kevin Knight

DESIGNER   Jane Hawkins

ILLUSTRATORS

Melvyn Evans (colour)

Marta Munoz (black and white)

Printed in China

Colour origination by Ivy Press Reprographics

10 9 8 7 6 5 4 3 2

MYTHS
IN 30 SECONDS

ANITA GANERI

Ivy Kids

Contents

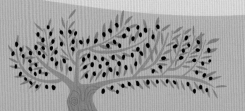

About this book
...in 60 seconds

For thousands of years, people from all cultures have told stories to make sense of the world around them. These stories are called myths. This book is a collection of 30 famous world myths, each retold in a shortened form.

Myths are not based on fact. Many tell stories about ancient people's beliefs, and the gods and goddesses they worshipped. Although some mythical gods seemed very human-like, they had a powerful influence on the world. Before people understood the science of natural events – such as thunderstorms, floods, a sunset, or even a good harvest – they believed that the gods caused them.

At first, many myths were not written down. Instead poets and storytellers remembered and retold them to the next generation. Later, ancient scribes began to write down traditional stories.

Writers from Ancient Greece, Ancient Rome, China and India have left accounts of their most important myths for future generations to read. In other cultures, such as African, Native American and Aboriginal, the myths are still passed on orally today.

You don't have to race through each myth in this book in just 30 seconds. Read them as quickly or as slowly as you want. You could even read them aloud, like a traditional storyteller. Have a good, long look at the beautiful illustrations too, and get ready to do the quests you'll find throughout.

Creation myths

Long before people understood how the world began, they had myths to explain how things were created. These told of the beginnings of the Earth and the appearance of the first people, plants and animals. In many myths, the land and sea were formed from chaos or nothingness by a great god or spirit. In this chapter, you can read creation myths of frost giants, jewelled spears, diving birds and heavenly chains.

Creation myths
Glossary

Buri The first god in Norse mythology.

frost giants Huge, supernatural beings in Norse myths. They were made of ice and were amazingly strong.

Ginnungagap (gin-un-ga-gap) In Norse myths, a vast empty space between **Muspell** and **Niflheim** before the world was created.

god A magical male being, worshipped as a creator or controller of the world, or of people's lives.

goddess A female god.

Izanagi In Japanese myths, the god who created the first land on Earth. The husband of **Izanami**.

Izanami In Japanese myths, the goddess who created the first land on Earth. The wife of **Izanagi**.

Maheo In Native American myths, the great spirit who created the Earth.

Mictlantecuhtli (mic-tlan-te-coo-tlee) In Aztec myths, the god of death and Lord of Mictlan, the Land of the Dead.

Muspell In Norse myths, a land of fire.

Niflheim (nee-ful-hym) In Norse myths, a land of ice and darkness and the location of Hel, Land of the Dead.

Obatala In West African myths, the god who came down from heaven to create the land and the first humans.

Odin In Norse myths, the king of the gods and god of war, battle and poetry. Odin was all-seeing and all-powerful.

Olokun In West African myths, a great goddess who ruled the sea and water.

Olorun In West African myths, a great god who ruled the sky.

Quetzalcoatl (ket-zal-co-atl) In Aztec myths, the god of the wind and the West who appeared as a cross between a bird and a snake.

Rainbow Bridge of Heaven In Japanese myths, a bridge connecting heaven and Earth.

Underworld Regions below the Earth, where people's souls went after death.

Ymir (ee-mair) In Norse myths, the first frost giant who was killed by **Odin**. The Earth was formed from his body.

How the world was made

...in 30 seconds (Norse)

Long ago, there were two realms: icy Niflheim in the north, and fiery Muspell in the south. Between the two lay a huge stretch of nothingness, called Ginnungagap.

Eleven rivers flowed from Niflheim into Ginnungagap, where they froze solid. When the ice neared the flames of Muspell, it melted. From the drops, two creatures were formed – the frost giant Ymir, and a huge cow, Audumla.

While Ymir slept, he sweated and, from his sweat, more frost giants appeared.

As Audumla licked the ice, a man-like figure appeared – Buri. In time, Buri's son Bor married a frost giantess and had three sons: the gods, Odin, Vili and Ve. They hated the frost giants and killed Ymir.

The gods shaped the Earth from Ymir's flesh and the mountains from his bones. His teeth became rocks, his blood the seas and his skull the sky. That is how the world was made.

3-second sum-up

The Norse world was created from the body of the frost giant, Ymir

Ice and fire

The Norse myths were first written down in the 13th century in Iceland. This country's spectacular landscape includes frozen ice sheets, gigantic glaciers and fire-breathing volcanoes – just like icy Niflheim and fiery Muspell!

Izanagi and Izanami
...in 30 seconds (Japanese)

The world was divided into two: above was heaven, below was a drifting ocean. The god and goddess, Izanagi and Izanami, stood on the Rainbow Bridge of Heaven and stirred the water with a long, jewelled spear. When they lifted it out, a drop of water fell from it and formed Onogoro, the first solid land.

Izanagi and Izanami came to live on Onogoro. They had many children, who became the islands of Japan.

One day, tragedy struck and Izanami died. Heartbroken, Izanagi travelled to Yomi, the Land of the Dead, to beg Izanami to return.

Izanami agreed to ask the god of death if he would let her go. She warned her husband not to follow her but Izanagi could not help himself. He broke a tooth from his comb and lit it to make a torch. When the light fell on Izanami, Izanagi saw that her body was rotting away. He had lost her for ever.

3-second sum-up

Izanagi and Izanami formed the first land from a drop of sea water

Shinto

The myth of Izanagi and Izanami is from the ancient Shinto religion of Japan. Its followers believe in spirits, called *kami*, which live in animals, plants and natural places, such as rivers and mountains. The most important *kami* is Amaterasu, the goddess of the Sun.

The Earth diver
...in 30 seconds (Native American)

In the beginning, the great spirit Maheo created a vast sea and all the creatures that lived in it. Fish swam under the water. Birds swam over the water.

One day, the birds came to Maheo. They asked him for a dry, solid place where they could walk, rest and build their nests.

Maheo agreed but said that he would need their help. He told them to take turns to dive to the bottom of the sea to look for land.

One by one, the birds dived down – first the snow goose, then the loon, then the mallard – but they brought nothing back. Finally, it was the coot's turn. When the bird surfaced, it was holding a little ball of mud in its beak.

Maheo rolled and kneaded the mud to form the land, until the ball was so big that only one creature was strong enough to carry it. And that is how old Grandmother Turtle came to carry the world on her back.

3-second sum-up

A bird helped the Great Spirit to create the land from a ball of mud

3-minute Quest
Who was Atlas?

In Greek mythology, the giant Atlas carries the world on his back. Find out:

1 Why Atlas must support the world.
2 How Atlas nearly tricks Heracles.

How would YOU have tricked Heracles?

Obatala's chain
...in 30 seconds (West African)

Once, there was only sky above and water below.
The great god, Olorun, ruled the sky. The great goddess, Olokun, ruled the water. Another god, Obatala, asked Olorun for permission to create dry land. The gods gave Obatala a long gold chain, and a bag containing a snail's shell filled with sand, a white hen, a black cat and a palm nut.

Obatala put the bag over his shoulder and hung the chain from a corner of the sky. Then he began to climb down.

Near the bottom, Obatala poured the sand from the snail's shell and let the hen go. The hen scratched and scrabbled at the sand and scattered it about to make the land. Obatala planted the palm nut and watched it grow into a tree. But Obatala was lonely with only the cat for company. He dug up some clay and moulded it into figures. Then he called on Olorun to breathe life into them, and they became the first people on Earth.

3-second sum-up

The god Obatala climbed down from heaven and made the land and people

3-minute quest News story!

Turn the myth of Obatala's chain into an amazing news story! Start with an eye-catching headline that will grab everyone's attention.

Why not include interviews with the hen, the cat and the first people on Earth?

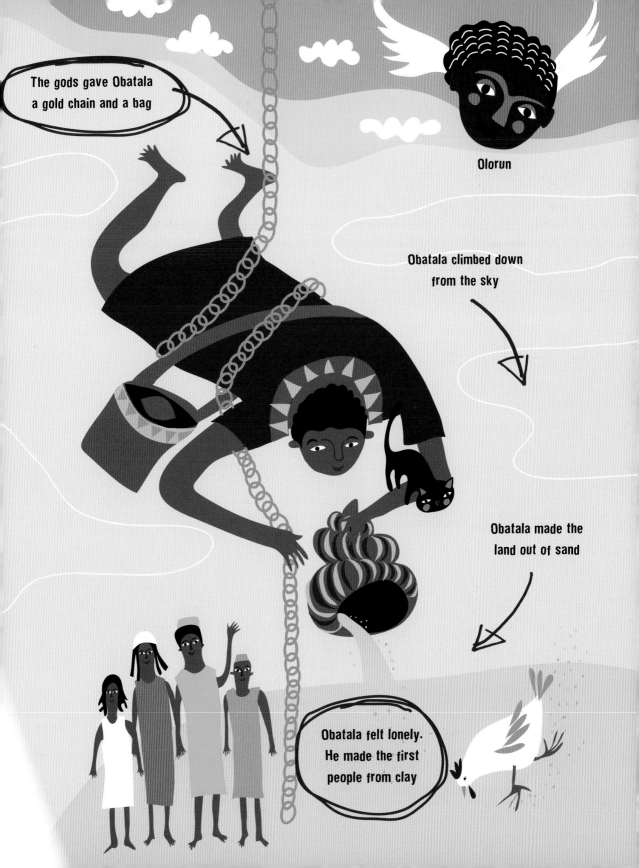

The wind god and the bones

...in 30 seconds (Aztec)

When the new world was created, there were no humans.
The last people on Earth had been turned into fish during a great flood. To make new people, the gods needed their bones.

Brave Quetzalcoatl, god of the wind, went to the Land of the Dead to fetch them. There, he came face to face with Mictlantecuhtli, the terrifying Lord of Death. Devious Mictlantecuhtli agreed to hand over the bones, on one condition:a

He told Quetzalcoatl to ride around the Underworld four times, blowing a conch-shell trumpet.

But the conch shell he gave to Quetzalcoatl had no holes, so could not make a sound. Quetzalcoatl asked some worms to bore holes in the shell and some bees to swarm around inside. When he blew the shell, it made a loud buzzing sound.

Back on Earth, Quetzalcoatl gave the bones to the goddess, Cihuacoatl, who ground them up and mixed them with blood from the gods. The gods watched until the first man and woman appeared.

3-second sum-up

Quetzalcoatl, the wind god, made people from bones from the Land of the Dead

Human sacrifice

The Aztec religion was very bloodthirsty. To ensure the sun rose every day, the Aztecs believed the all-powerful Sun god, Huitzilopochtli (*hweet-seelo-potch-tli*), needed a regular supply of human blood. A priest would cut the heart from the chest of the chosen victim and hold it up to the sun.

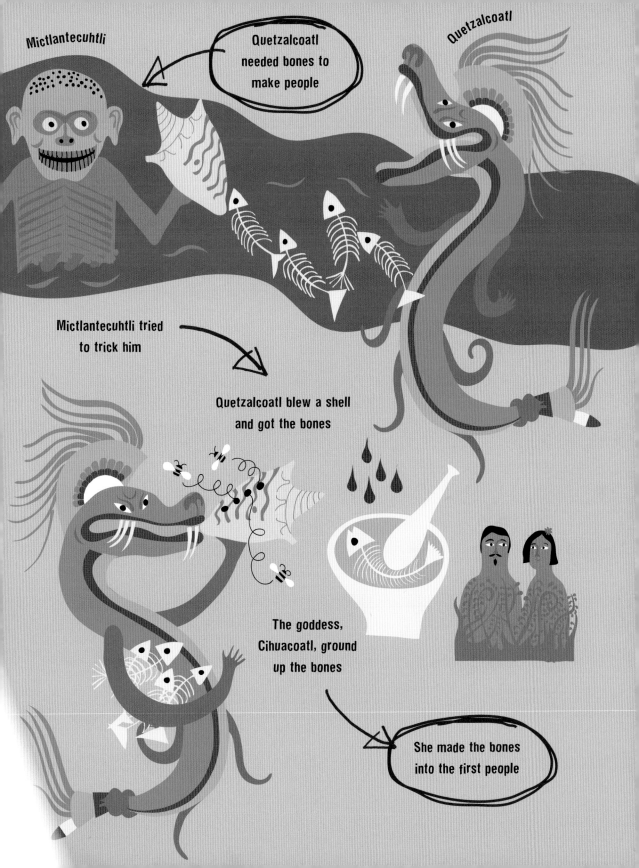

Gods and goddesses

In ancient times gods and goddesses were believed to control people's lives and all the good and bad things that happened to them, and to their world. Some gods and goddesses were distant figures but others behaved more like human beings – they had arguments, married and had children, played tricks on each other, and had adventures. In this chapter, you can read tales of gods and goddesses who fell in love, slayed monstrous demons, competed for a city, caused the Sun to go out, and fooled a thieving giant.

Gods and goddesses
Glossary

Amaterasu In Japanese myths, the goddess of the Sun. Daughter of Izanami and Izanagi, and sister of **Susano**.

Diana In Roman myths, the goddess of the Moon and hunting. Daughter of **Jupiter**, she carried a silver bow and arrow.

Durga In Hindu myths, a fearsome goddess with countless arms holding weapons. She rode on a lion or tiger.

dwarves In many myths, small magical beings with enormous strength. They are often brave warriors and skilled metalworkers.

Endymion In Roman myths, a handsome shepherd. The goddess, **Diana**, fell in love with him.

Freyja (frey-a) In Norse myths, the goddess of love, beauty and fertility. She owned a magic falcon skin that allowed her to fly.

Jupiter In Roman myths, the all-powerful king of the gods. He was also god of thunder and lightning.

Mahisha In Hindu myths, a demon who could change from a buffalo to a human in a flash. In the end he was killed by the goddess **Durga**.

Minerva In Roman myths, the goddess of wisdom and war. The daughter of **Jupiter**, she always wore armour.

Mjollnir (mule-nir) In Norse myths, **Thor**'s magic war hammer that had been made by the **dwarves**. A fearsome weapon, it always hit its target and always came back to Thor.

Neptune In Roman myths, the god of the sea. The brother of **Jupiter**, he carried a **trident**.

Omoikane In Japanese myths, the god of wisdom and intelligence.

Susano In Japanese myths, the god of storms and the sea. The son of **Izanami** and **Izanagi**, and the brother of **Amaterasu**.

Thor In Norse myths, the son of Odin (king of the Norse gods), and god of thunder, law and order. A great warrior, Thor was also the defender of Asgard, home of the gods.

Thrym In Norse myths, the giant who stole **Thor**'s hammer and paid for the theft with his life.

trident A three-pronged spear.

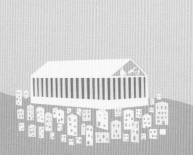

Diana and the shepherd boy
...in 30 seconds (Roman)

Diana, goddess of hunting and the Moon, drove across the sky in a chariot, pulled by white deer. One night, as she looked down to Earth, she saw a handsome young man sleeping on a hillside. He was Endymion, a shepherd. Diana fell in love with him at first sight. She stepped down from her chariot, kissed him, then drove away again.

Half awake, Endymion caught a glimpse of the goddess but when he got up, all he could see was the Moon floating in the dark sky.

Every night, Diana visited him as he slept, and every night, Endymion saw her dazzling beauty through half-closed eyes. But Diana was filled with dread that Endymion would lose his looks as he got older. She cast a spell on him so that he would never wake up again. Then she carried him to a cave in a mountainside. There, she would stop on her nightly journey across the sky to gaze on his handsome face.

3-second sum-up

The Moon goddess, Diana, fell in love with the shepherd, Endymion

Roman gods

The Romans admired Greek religion and mythology, and many Roman myths came from Greek ones. The Romans even took over the Greek gods and gave them Roman names.

Greek	Roman
Artemis	Diana
Pluto	Dis
Demeter	Ceres
Zeus	Jupiter
Persephone	Proserpina

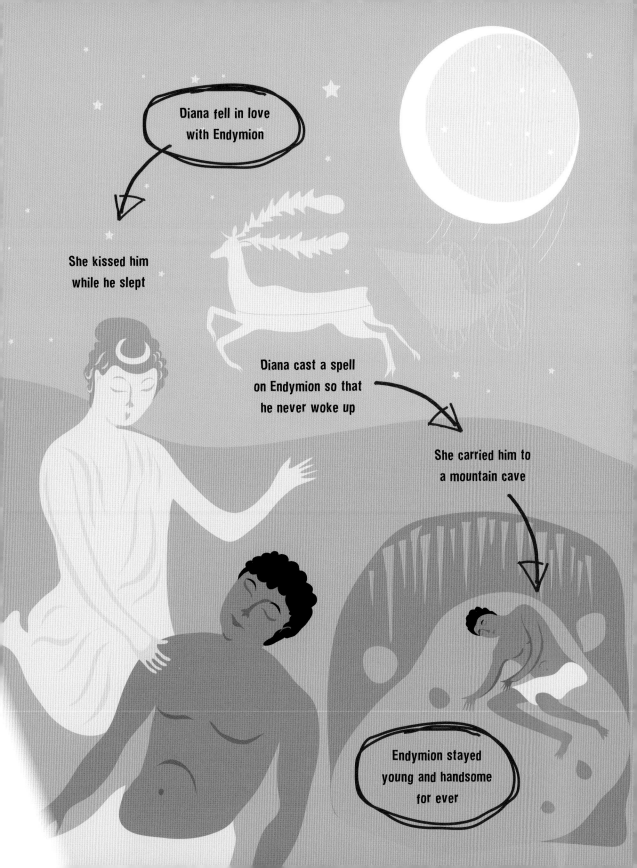

Durga and the buffalo demon

...in 30 seconds (Indian)

Mahisha was a terrible demon who had been granted a special favour. He would be able to live for ever unless he was killed by a woman. Thinking himself to be all-powerful, Mahisha and his demon army attacked heaven and, after a fierce battle, threw the gods out of their home.

In dismay, the gods met and summoned their powers to call for help. A blinding light appeared and, out of it, rode Durga, the goddess of war, mounted on a lion.

The gods gave Durga their deadliest weapons, which she held in her many hands. Then she confronted Mahisha. His demon warriors launched a fierce attack but Durga killed them, one by one, until only Mahisha was left. Quickly, Mahisha turned himself into a gigantic buffalo, and charged. As he came closer, Durga took her chance. She pinned the buffalo down and cut off its head. And so Mahisha was killed by a woman, and peace and harmony returned to the world.

3-second sum-up

Durga, goddess of war, fought and killed the buffalo demon, Mahisha

3-minute quest Plan a movie

Turn the story of Durga and the buffalo demon into a mini-movie:

- Draw a storyboard of the plot, scene by scene.
- Write the dialogue and plan the special effects.

Which part would YOU play?

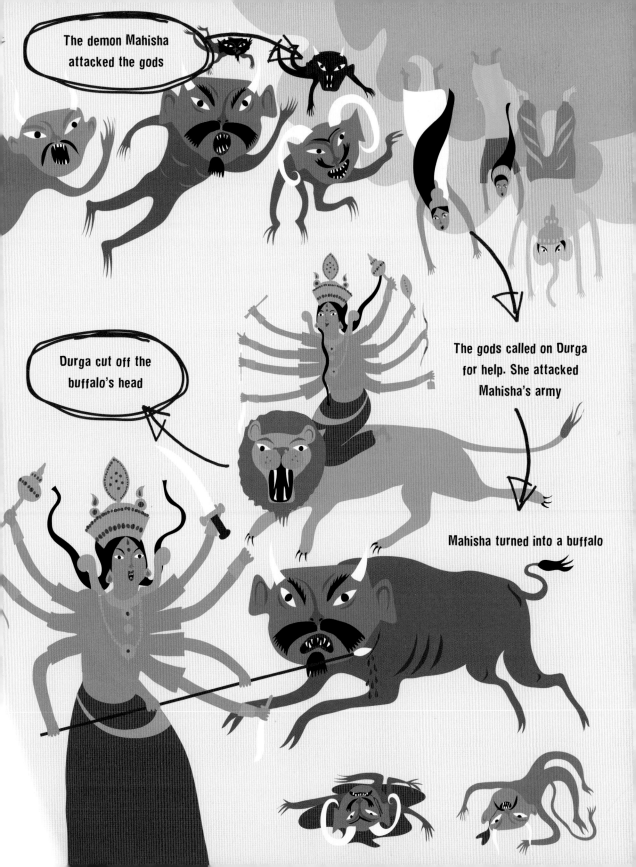

Neptune and Minerva

...in 30 seconds (Roman)

Once, Neptune, god of the sea, and Minerva, goddess of wisdom and war, quarrelled about which of them should have the honour of claiming a new city in Greece. King of the gods, Jupiter, decided that the winner should be the one who gave the city the best gift. He and the gods would judge the contest.

Neptune tapped the side of a mountain with his trident and a great stream gushed out. It gave the town fresh water and a way to reach the sea. Surely, he would win?

Then Minerva waved her hand and an olive tree began to grow. At first, the gods laughed scornfully but they soon changed their minds. The tree produced tasty olives and olive oil for eating, and fine wood for building. In time, the people of the city grew rich by selling the olives and wood abroad. It was a magnificent gift and the gods judged that Minerva had won. The city was hers.

3-second sum-up

Neptune and Minerva went head-to-head to claim a new city

3-minute quest Talk show!

Get a friend to play Minerva while you play a famous talk-show host. Introduce her with a big build up and ask her questions, including:

- How do you feel now that you've won?
- What made you think of an olive tree?
- Was Neptune a good loser?

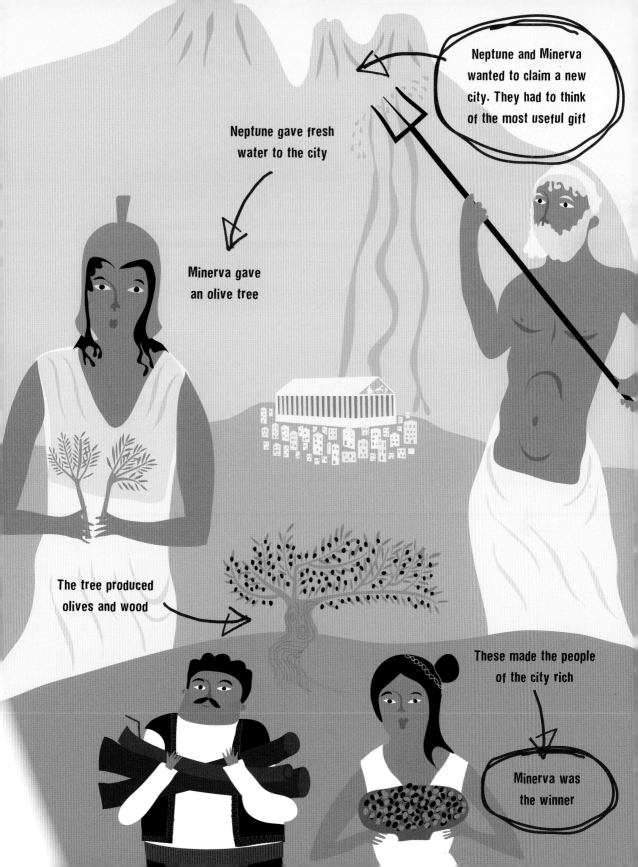

The day the Sun went out

...in 30 seconds (Japanese)

Susano, the storm god, could not stop weeping when his mother, Izanami, died. His father banished him to the Underworld to join Izanami.

Before Susano left, he asked to visit his sister, the Sun goddess Amaterasu, in the sacred weaving hall. The two had a terrible quarrel. In his rage, Susano picked up a horse and hurled it through the roof of the hall.

Gentle Amaterasu was so frightened that she ran away and hid in a deep, dark cave. As Amaterasu hid, the Sun went out and the world was plunged into darkness.

Thinking quickly, the god Omoikane hung a magic rope of jewels and a magic mirror from a tree outside the cave. The goddess of dawn started dancing around.

Amaterasu peeked out to have a look and was dazzled by her reflection in the mirror. At once, the gods pulled her out of the cave and blocked the entrance with the magic rope. So the Sun returned to the world.

3-second sum-up

The gods tricked Amaterasu out of hiding so that the Sun could shine again

3-minute Quest Sun gods

Ra (Ancient Egypt), Apollo (Greek) and Surya (Indian) were Sun gods from other ancient cultures. See if you can find out:

1 What bird is connected with Ra.
2 Apollo's other name.
3 How Surya travelled across the sky.

Thor's lost hammer

...in 30 seconds (Norse)

Thor, god of thunder, owned a fearsome war hammer, Mjollnir, forged for him by the dwarves. When thrown, it always hit its target, then returned to Thor's hand. It had protective powers and was used at weddings to bless the bride.

Once, in a fit of jealousy, the giant, Thrym, stole Mjollnir. He told Thor that he would return the hammer but only if he could marry the beautiful goddess, Freyja.

Freyja refused. So the god Heimdall came up with a plan. Thor would dress up as a bride and pretend to be Freyja. Then he could steal the hammer back.

Thor arrived at Thrym's hall wearing a wedding dress and a long veil to hide his face. But he almost gave himself away by the amount he ate and drank.

Soon, Thrym called for Mjollnir to be brought out to bless the bride. At once, Thor grabbed the hammer and ripped off his disguise. He raised Mjollnir and killed Thrym with a crushing blow.

3-second sum-up

Thor disguised himself as a bride to win back his stolen hammer

Thor, god of thunder!

Thor's big personality matched his large size. He had wild red hair, a red beard, a fiery temper and he couldn't stay quiet for even a minute. He did everything in a big, noisy way – fighting, feasting and drinking too much beer. Even so, he was also the god of law and order, protector of gods and humans.

Heroes and tricksters

Heroes in myths are mostly brave and good. They perform great deeds and give important gifts to humankind, such as knowledge. Tricksters do the opposite – they bring chaos and confusion, especially to the well-ordered world of the gods. In this chapter, you can read tales of heroes who battled nine-headed monsters and caught magical fish, and tricksters who stole fire from the Sun, beat the gods at games, and tried to hide the pot of wisdom.

Heroes and tricksters
Glossary

Anansi In African myths, a spider character who could also appear as a man. He was famous for playing tricks and getting into mischief.

Cerberus In Greek myths, a monstrous, three-headed dog that guarded the gates of the Underworld (where people's souls went after death).

Eurystheus (Eur-is-the-us) In Greek myths, a king and also the grandson of the hero Perseus.

Finn MacCool In Irish myths, a great hero and giant who was the leader of a group of brave warriors, called the Fianna.

Hera In Greek myths, the queen of the gods and wife of **Zeus**, who was worshipped as a goddess of marriage and birth. She was jealous of Zeus's many love affairs.

Heracles In Greek myths, a great hero and **Zeus**'s son by Alceme, a mortal (human) woman. He was famous for his strength and for performing 12 dangerous and difficult tasks.

Hunahpu (hoo-na-poo) In Mayan myths, one of the Hero Twins who outwitted the gods of death.

Lernaean (ler-nay-an) hydra In Greek myths, a terrible, snake-like monster with many heads that grew again when they were cut off. The hydra was killed by **Heracles**.

Nemean (ne-may-an) lion
In Greek myths, a terrifying golden-furred lion. Its skin was so tough that arrows and swords bounced off it.

Nyame In African myths, a great god of the sky. His right eye was the Sun; his left eye was the Moon.

Olympian In Greek myths, any of the 12 gods who lived on Mount Olympus.

Prometheus In Greek myths, the son of a **Titan**. He stole fire from the gods to help humans and was punishedby **Zeus**.

Titans In Greek myths, 12 god-like giants (6 brothers and 6 sisters) who ruled the Earth before the gods.

Xbalanque (sh-blan-kay) In Mayan myths, one of the Hero Twins who outwitted the gods of death.

Xibalba (shi-bal-ba) In Mayan myths, the terrifying Underworld (where people's souls went after death).

Zeus In Greek myths, the all-powerful king of the gods. He ruled from Mount Olympus and also controlled thunder and lightning.

Prometheus steals fire

...in 30 seconds (Greek)

Prometheus, son of a Titan, was given the job of helping to decide how meat from sacrifices should be shared between the Olympian gods and humans. Prometheus had a clever plan to make sure humankind had plenty of food. He sorted the meat from a slaughtered ox into two piles. The first was a pile of bones covered in tasty-looking fat, and the second was delicious meat hidden away inside the ox's stomach. Zeus was fooled, and chose the bones, leaving the meat for humankind.

Zeus was furious with Prometheus for his trickery. As a punishment, he took away fire from humankind.

People were forced to live in cold darkness, and could not cook the meat Prometheus had given them. Zeus's cruelty angered Prometheus. He daringly stole fire from the Sun in a giant fennel stalk, and gave it to the people. But Prometheus suffered a gruesome punishment for his disloyalty. Zeus had him tied to the side of a mountain and tortured by a massive eagle that ate his liver daily.

3-second sum-up

Prometheus stole fire from the gods to give to humans, and was punished

3-minute Quest
Find the fire-stealers

Like Prometheus, fire-stealers in many world myths take fire from the gods to help humanity. Find out who steals fire according to Cherokee Native American stories. Are there any more you can find from other cultures?

Prometheus tricked the gods
Angry Zeus took fire away from humans
Prometheus stole fire from the Sun
As punishment, Zeus had Prometheus tied to a mountain. Every day, an eagle ripped out bits of his liver

The labours of Heracles

...in 30 seconds (Greek)

The goddess, Hera, tricked Heracles into killing his wife and children. As punishment, King Eurystheus set Heracles 12 seemingly impossible labours, or tasks. The first was to kill the Nemean lion, a beast with skin so tough that no weapon could pierce it. Heracles stunned the lion with his club, then strangled it with his bare hands. Afterwards, he always wore the lion's skin to protect him from harm.

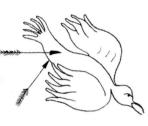

Next, Heracles had to slay the Lernaean hydra, a monster with nine heads and deadly poisonous breath. He sealed each head as he cut it off to stop it growing back again.

Among his other tasks, Heracles had to trap an enormous boar, kill a flock of man-eating birds and round up a herd of wild horses. For his 12th and final task, he managed to capture Cerberus, the fierce, three-headed dog that guarded the gates of the Underworld. His tasks successfully completed, Heracles was freed from his dreadful guilt and granted immortality – he would live for ever.

3-second sum-up

Heracles completed 12 deadly tasks as a punishment and became immortal

3-minute quest Hero profile

Find out more about Heracles then fill in his hero profile, using these headings:

Birthplace	Best quest
Parents	Worst quest
Job	Strength
Favourite weapon	Weakness

Hero Twins and the ball game
...in 30 seconds (Mayan)

The gods Xbalanque and Hunahpu were the Hero Twins. They longed to avenge the death of their father, who had been killed by the lords of Xibalba, the Underworld.

One day, the lords challenged them to a ball game. First, the Twins made the terrifying journey to Xibalba, down steep cliffs, across rivers of blood, and through the Houses of Gloom, Knives, Cold and Bats.

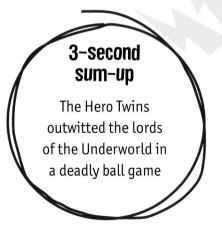

In the House of Bats, a giant bat snatched Hunahpu's head and carried it off to the lords. Xbalanque made his brother a new head from a large squash.

In the game, the lords used Hunahpu's real head as the ball until Xbalanque hurled it out of court. While the lords looked for it, Xbalanque switched it for the squash. As soon as the game began again the squash split.

The furious lords tried to kill the Twins, but instead the Twins killed them. Victorious, the Twins rose into the sky, and became the Sun and the Moon.

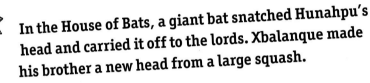

3-second sum-up

The Hero Twins outwitted the lords of the Underworld in a deadly ball game

3-minute quest
Invent a game

In ancient times, people invented games, and made bats, balls and other equipment from whatever they could find. Invent your own bizarre ballgame to play, using objects you can find around the house. Name your game and make up a set of rules.

Anansi and the world's wisdom

...in 30 seconds (African)

Long ago, people could not plant crops, weave clothes or make metal tools. The great god, Nyame, was keeper of all the wisdom in the world, stored in a clay pot.

One day, Nyame gave the pot to Anansi, the spider man. Greedy Anansi wanted to keep all the wisdom to himself. He decided to hide the pot at the top of a tall tree.

Anansi made a rope from vines and tied the pot to his waist. Then he began to climb the tree.

Climbing was hard with the pot dangling in front of him, and Anansi began to feel annoyed. His young son told him to tie the pot to his back instead. This made climbing much easier but Anansi was still cross. How come his little son was cleverer than him?

In a fit of temper, Anansi threw the pot to the ground, where it smashed. And all the wisdom inside blew far and wide across the world.

3-second sum-up

Anansi's anger and greed caused wisdom to be scattered across the world

3-minute Quest
Mischief makers

Raven, from Native American mythology, and Loki, from Norse mythology are two other brave, cunning tricksters.

Choose one of these mischief makers, and find out what tricks they used.

Finn and the fish of knowledge

...in 30 seconds (Irish)

When the great hero and giant, Finn MacCool, was young, he went to visit a wise poet and teacher who lived by a spring, called the Well of Seghais. For seven years, the poet had waited to catch the magical salmon of knowledge that lived in the waters of the well.

It was said that eating this fish would bring a person all the knowledge in the world.

One day, the poet caught the salmon. He gave it to Finn to cook but ordered him not to eat any of it.

Finn cooked the salmon, but burnt his thumb on its skin. He put his thumb in his mouth and immediately felt himself becoming wiser. When the poet found out, he told Finn to eat the salmon – for the knowledge must be meant for him.

So Finn ate the salmon of knowledge, and whenever he needed to call on its magical powers, he had only to put his thumb in his mouth.

3-second sum-up

Finn accidentally tasted the magical salmon and gained all knowledge

The Giant's Causeway

The Giant's Causeway in Northern Ireland is made of thousands of columns of volcanic rock stretching out to sea. A myth says that it was formed when Finn McCool got into a fight with a rival giant and hurled huge rocks across the sea at him.

Quests and adventures

In mythology, many heroes have great quests and adventures and face danger, disaster and death. Some set off to find a magical or holy object. Others are looking for something even more precious: the secret of immortality – everlasting life. In this chapter, you can read tales of brave quests for a plant that granted immortality and a priceless Golden Fleece, a daring voyage to found a new city, and a fateful journey from which the travellers were never allowed to return.

Quests and adventures
Glossary

Aeneas (ay-nay-us) In Roman myths, the son of the goddess Aphrodite, a great hero and warrior who defended the city of **Troy** in the Trojan War.

Argonauts In Greek myths, the band of human heroes who were **Jason**'s crew on board the **_Argo_**.

Argo In Greek myths, **Jason**'s ship on which he sailed in search of the **Golden Fleece**.

Bran In Irish myths, a great hero who travelled to a magic land and could never again return home.

Colchis An ancient kingdom on the Black Sea coast in modern-day Georgia.

Dido In Roman myths, the Queen of Carthage (in modern-day Tunisia), who fell in love with **Aeneas**.

Gilgamesh In Sumerian myths, a great hero and king of **Uruk**.

Golden Fleece In Greek myths, the fleece of a golden-haired, winged ram that once belonged to the goddess, Hera.

Harpies In Greek myths, monstrous birds with women's heads. They carried away their human victims and drove them mad with their screeching.

immortality Living for ever.

Iolcus In Greek myths, an ancient city in eastern Greece. **Jason** set sail from here to search for the **Golden Fleece**.

Jason In Greek myths, a great hero who went on a dangerous journey to bring the **Golden Fleece** back from **Colchis**.

Mesopotamia An ancient land in the Middle East, between the Tigris and Euphrates rivers. The Sumerian people lived here.

prophetess A woman who could foretell the future.

Sibyl In Greek myths, the name for a **prophetess**.

Sidhe In Irish myths, a race of immortals who lived on a group of magical islands, called the Happy Otherworld.

Troy In Greek myths, the setting for the Trojan War. The ruins of this ancient city are in north-west Turkey.

Uruk An important Sumerian city in ancient **Mesopotamia**.

Utnapishtim (ut-na-pish-tim) In Sumerian myths, the only survivor of the Great Flood, who told **Gilgamesh** where to find a plant that had the power to grant immortality.

The voyage of Aeneas

...in 30 seconds (Roman)

After defeat in the Trojan War, the prince Aeneas fled Troy with a group of trusted companions and set sail to found a new city, as the gods had foretold.

The first part of his voyage lasted six long years, before his ships were wrecked near the city of Carthage, off the coast of North Africa. There, Aeneas fell in love with Queen Dido, who wanted him to stay and rule with her.

Soon, though, the gods reminded Aeneas of his destiny and he left Carthage to continue his travels. Heartbroken, Dido killed herself.

Next, Aeneas sailed to Cumae, Italy, where he met the Sibyl, a prophetess who guarded a cave at the entrance to the Underworld. She led him down into the Underworld and showed him a vision of the future – the city of Rome.

Finally, Aeneas reached Latium where he fulfilled his destiny and married Lavinia, the daughter of the local king. Legend says that his descendants founded mighty Rome in Latium.

3-second sum-up

After fleeing Troy, Aeneas eventually reached Italy, where his descendants founded Rome

3-minute Quest
Discover the monsters!

On his journey to Cumae, Aeneas and his crew met two terrible monsters. The first was Charybdis and the second was a giant called a Cyclops. See if you can find out what was so scary about these deadly creatures.

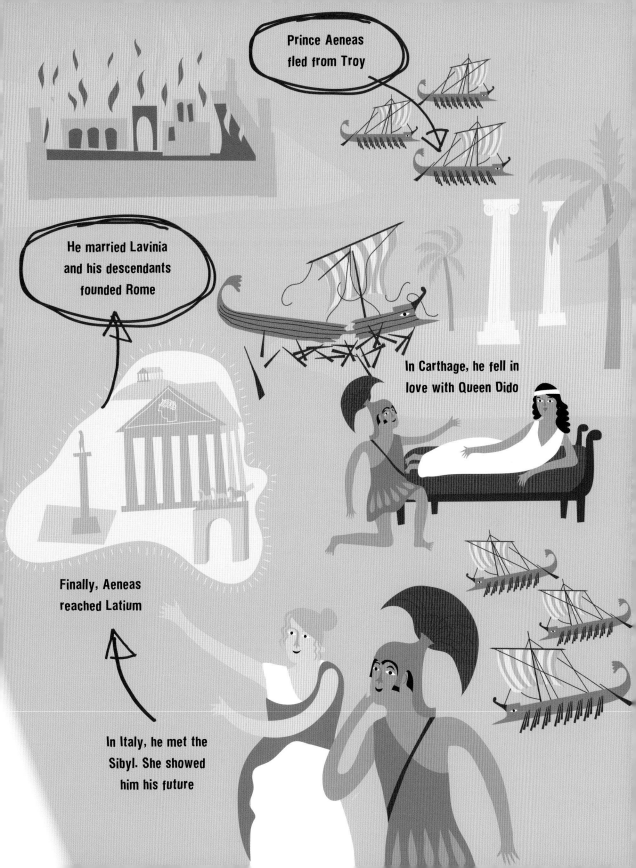

Jason and the Golden Fleece
...in 30 seconds (Greek)

Greek hero, Jason, was the rightful heir to the throne of Iolcus but his uncle, Pelias, seized power. Pelias agreed to return the crown on condition that Jason bring back the priceless Golden Fleece from Colchis – a seemingly impossible task.

Jason had a fine ship built, the *Argo*, and gathered a group of heroes, the Argonauts, to accompany him.

The journey was filled with danger. The Argonauts had to destroy the Harpies (monstrous birds with women's heads). They had to navigate their way through the Clashing Rocks, gigantic cliffs that crushed ships by slamming together.

In Colchis, the king set Jason a series of trials. First, Jason had to plough a field with a pair of fire-breathing bulls. Then he had to fight an army of warriors. Finally, with the help of the king's daughter, Medea, Jason overcame the dragon that guarded the fleece by lulling it to sleep. At last, he was able to seize the fleece and sail for home.

3-second sum-up

Jason and the Argonauts faced terrible dangers before seizing the Golden Fleece

Jason's end

Jason had promised to love Medea for ever but left her for Glauce, the King of Corinth's daughter. Medea got her revenge: she gave Glauce a poisoned dress, which killed her, and also her father. Medea also killed the two sons she bore Jason. Unhappy and alone, Jason was killed while sleeping under the *Argo*, when rotting timbers fell on top of him.

Jason set sail on the *Argo*

He destroyed the Harpies

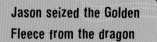
Jason seized the Golden Fleece from the dragon

He tamed the fire-breathing bulls

The king's daughter, Medea, helped him to defeat the dragon

The voyage of Bran

...in 30 seconds (Celtic)

Long ago, the hero, Bran, held a great feast in his hall. A beautiful woman appeared and sang about a group of strangers who would visit a magical land where there was no illness and death.

Bran decided to make the journey, along with 30 companions. Several days later, they reached the magical islands of the Happy Otherworld, a place of great peace and happiness, and home to a race of immortals, called the Sidhe.

After a year, one of Bran's companions, Nechtan, felt homesick and persuaded the others to return to Ireland. But the Sidhe gave them a dire warning. On no account should the men try to set foot on Irish soil again.

As soon as they neared the Irish shore, Nechtan leapt from the ship and ran up the beach. But, as he ran, his body turned to dust. This is what the Sidhe's warning had meant. Sadly, Bran ordered the ship to turn around and they sailed away, never to be seen again.

3-second sum-up

Bran visited the Happy Otherworld but could never return home again

3-minute quest
Create a comic

Turn Bran's quest into a comic strip.

- Plan the picture frames first.
- Add speech bubbles to show what the characters are saying.
- Add extra text flashes to help explain the story, or to move the plot along.

Bran sailed to the Happy Otherworld
It was a happy, peaceful place
Nechtan felt homesick
The Sidhe warned Bran not to try to land in Ireland
Bran and his companions sailed back to Ireland
Nechtan tried to land and turned to dust

The quest of Gilgamesh

...in 30 seconds (Sumerian)

Gilgamesh was king of Uruk, one of the greatest cities of ancient Mesopotamia. Part god and part human, he was doomed, like all humans, to die one day. Seeing Enkidu, his best friend, die made Gilgamesh very afraid.

He set out on a great quest to discover the secret of immortality. First, he searched out Utnapishtim, the survivor of the Great Flood.

Utnapishtim told Gilgamesh about a plant that grew at the bottom of a lake in the Underworld and made people young again.

Hearing this, Gilgamesh tied heavy stones to his feet, which dragged him down to the Underworld. With the help of Urshanabi, the ferryman, Gilgamesh found the plant and set off for Uruk to share it with his people.

On the way, he stopped for the night and went to bathe in a stream. While he was gone, a snake stole the precious plant and carried it away. Gilgamesh returned home a broken man, his chance of immortality lost for ever.

3-second sum-up

Gilgamesh found the secret of immortality but a snake stole it

Immortals

There are many myths about people living for ever. In Chinese myth, Queen Xi Wangmu, the wife of the Emperor of Heaven, grants immortality by giving a person a special potion or one of the peaches of immortality that grows in her garden.

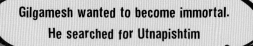

Gilgamesh wanted to become immortal.
He searched for Utnapishtim

Utnapishtim told
Gilgamesh to
journey to the
Underworld

Gilgamesh found
a magic plant
that would make
him young again

On the way home, a
snake stole the plant

Earth, water and sky

Ancient people were mystified by nature. Everything they saw, from sunrise or sunset to high mountains or a rushing river, seemed magical to them. They believed that all these things had been created by the gods, and told myths to explain them. In this chapter, you can read tales of how the seasons came to be, the ten deadly suns, the god who caught a river, the rabbit in the Moon, the Rainbow Serpent, and of the thunder god kept in a cage.

Earth, water and sky
Glossary

Bhagiratha (bag-i-ratha) In Hindu myths, a great king who brought the **River Ganges** to Earth.

Ceres In Roman myths, goddess of the Earth and harvests who caused the crops to grow. The mother of **Proserpina**.

Dis In Roman myths, a god of the Underworld (where people's souls went after death) who kidnapped **Proserpina** and married her.

Dreamtime In Aboriginal myths, a sacred time long ago when spirits created the Earth.

Ganges, River A great river in India that is sacred in the Hindu religion.

Indra In the Hindu religion, the king of the gods, and god of war and thunderstorms.

Nanahuatzin (nana-wa-tsin) In Aztec myths, the god who becomes the Sun.

Proserpina In Roman myths, the beautiful daughter of **Ceres**, who was kidnapped by **Dis** and taken to the Underworld but allowed to live on Earth for part of the year.

Rainbow Serpent In Aboriginal myths, a serpent spirit that appeared as a rainbow in the sky.

Sakara In Hindu myths, an ancient king and great ruler. The grandfather of **Bhagiratha**.

Shiva In the Hindu religion, a great god who broke the fall of the **River Ganges** from heaven by catching it in his long hair.

Tecuciztecatl (tecu-sis-te-catl) In Aztec myths, the god who turns into the Moon.

thunder god In Chinese myths, a god who punished evil-doers.

Yi In Chinese myths, a great archer who shot down the nine suns and so managed to save the Earth.

Ceres and Proserpina
...in 30 seconds (Roman)

Ceres, goddess of plants, had a beautiful daughter, Proserpina. Dis, king of the Underworld, longed to marry Proserpina but he knew that Ceres would never agree.

One day, when Proserpina was picking flowers, Dis grabbed her and carried her away. Grief-stricken, Ceres searched for her daughter and neglected the plants she cared for. The crops died, the harvests failed and people began to starve.

Finally, Jupiter, king of the gods, agreed that Proserpina could return to Earth, as long as she had not eaten anything during her stay.

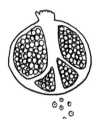

Proserpina had only eaten a few pomegranate seeds but that was enough to make a difference. Jupiter decreed that she should spend part of the year in the Underworld with Dis, and part on Earth with Ceres.

And that is how the seasons came to be. While Proserpina was away, Ceres mourned, the plants died and it was winter. When she returned, Ceres was happy, the plants bloomed and spring arrived.

3-second sum-up

Proserpina's kidnapping by the god of the Underworld led to the seasons

3-minute quest
Find the Greek myth

Look for the Greek myth that is similar to this Roman story. See if you can find:

- The Greek names for Ceres, Proserpina and Jupiter.
- Any other differences you can find between the two tales.

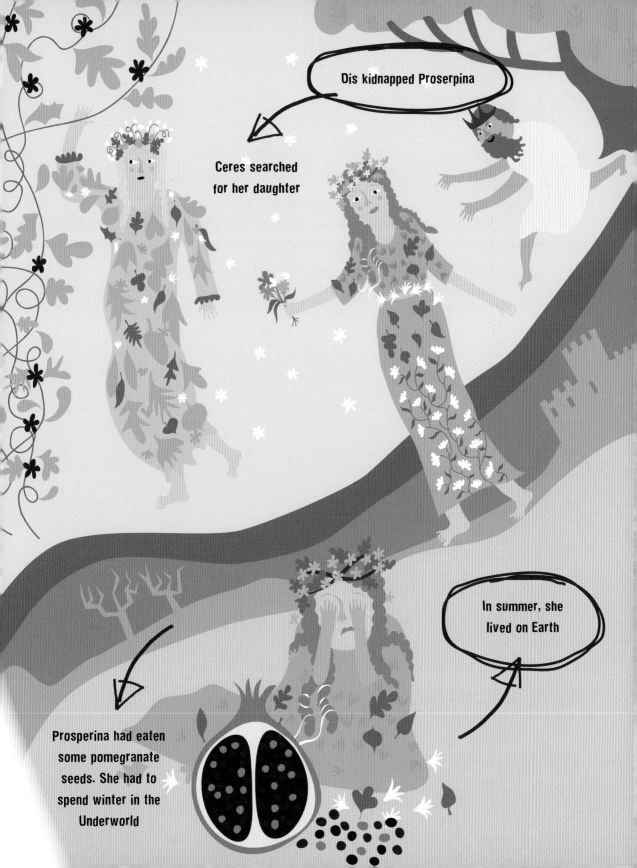

Yi shoots the suns

...in 30 seconds (Chinese)

Long ago, there were ten different suns in the sky which took it in turns to shine. This way, the Earth was warmed, crops grew and people lived happily.

One terrible day, all ten suns decided to shine at the same time. In the scorching heat, the Earth dried up, crops withered and people began to starve and die.

Seeing the suffering on Earth, the Lord of Heaven called for Yi, the archer, and sent him to shoot the suns down.

Yi took his bow and arrows, and took aim at the suns, one by one. When Yi shot the sixth sun, he still had four arrows left. Disaster loomed. If Yi shot all ten suns, the Earth would be plunged into darkness.

Silently, the Lord of Heaven took one of the arrows away. And so Yi, the archer, shot nine of the suns, leaving one to warm the Earth again. Soon, clouds formed, rain fell and the Earth was saved.

3-second sum-up

Yi, the archer, shot down nine of the ten suns to save the Earth

What happened to Yi?

The nine suns shot down by Yi were the children of Dijun, the God of the Eastern Heaven. Dijun was furious with Yi. He banished Yi and his wife (Chang E, the goddess of the Moon) from heaven and took away their immortality.

All ten suns shone together

One sun was left to warm the Earth

The Earth began to burn

The Lord of Heaven took his last arrow away

Yi, the archer, shot down the suns one by one

How the Ganges fell to Earth

...in 30 seconds (Indian)

King Sakara wanted to perform a horse sacrifice to show that he was the greatest ruler on Earth. He chose the most splendid horse in his kingdom for the ceremony.

But Indra, king of the gods, feared Sakara was growing too powerful. He stole the horse and hid it deep underground. At once, King Sakara's 60,000 sons set off to find the horse but were burnt to ashes by the heat from the centre of the Earth.

Years later, the king's grandson, Bhagiratha, vowed to bring his ancestors back to life. The only way to do this was to let the sacred River Ganges fall to Earth.

Bhagiratha prayed to the gods for help, and finally, they ordered the river to fall from heaven. But the force of the rushing water would have shattered the ground beneath its weight.

So Lord Shiva caught the river in his long, tangled hair and let it trickle down gently down to Earth. Then Bhagiratha led it underground, where it touched his ancestors' ashes and set them free.

3-second sum-up

Lord Shiva caught the River Ganges in his hair to break its fall from heaven to Earth

Sacred waters

For Hindus, the Ganges is a sacred river, worshipped as the goddess, Ganga. Believers make long journeys to places along the Ganges to bathe. They believe the waters will wash away their sins and set them free.

King Sakara's 60,000 sons died. His grandson, Bhagiratha, vowed to save them
The River Ganges fell from heaven
Lord Shiva
Lord Shiva broke the river's fall with his hair
The water flowed underground and set the sons free

The rabbit in the Moon

...in 30 seconds

After the Earth and sky had been formed, the gods met to decide who would become the new Sun and Moon. Two volunteers stepped forward – rich, proud Tecuciztecatl and poor, humble Nanahuatzin. The gods set the two a series of tasks to prove their worth. For the last, most deadly task the gods lit a blazing fire and ordered Tecuciztecatl and Nanahuatzin to jump into it.

Nanahuatzin rushed fearlessly into the flames at once. Tecuciztecatl tried and failed four times before following his rival into the fire.

So Nanahuatzin rose in the sky as the new Sun. He shone so brightly that the gods couldn't look at his face. Not to be outdone, Tecuciztecatl followed him into the sky as the Moon, shining so radiantly that the gods feared that he would outshine the Sun. So, one god threw a rabbit at the Moon to dim its light. This explains why you can see the shape of a rabbit on its surface.

3-second sum-up

Two rival Aztec gods competed in a deadly challenge to become the Sun and Moon

3-minute Quest
Who's in the Moon?

Look on the internet for a clear picture of the full Moon. Look at the shadows on its surface. Do you see a man or a rabbit in the dark shapes? Or maybe something completely different? Trace the outlines of your Moon figures on a printout, if you like.

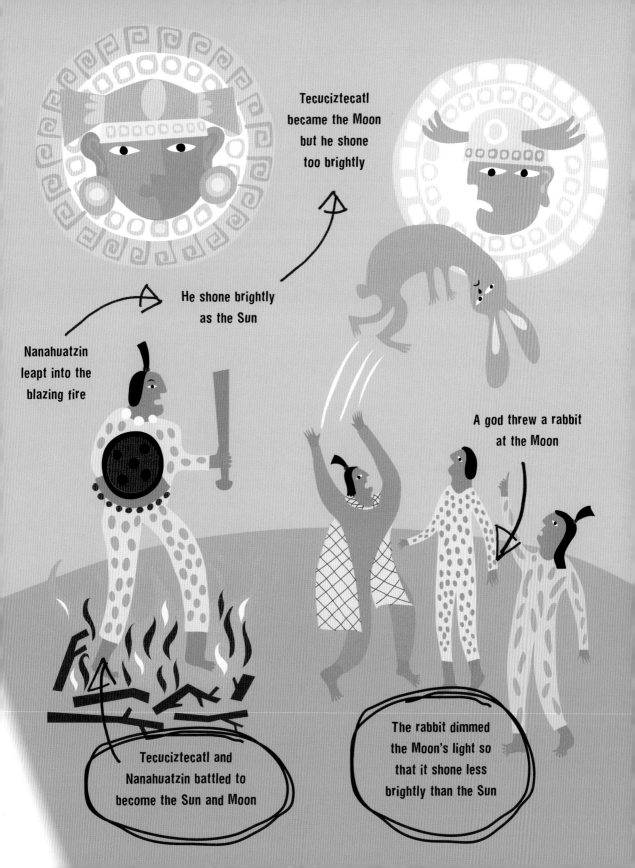

The Rainbow Serpent

...in 30 seconds (Aboriginal)

During a time long ago, called the Dreamtime, the rainbow turned into a serpent and slithered down to Earth. After a while, he reached a campfire. The people made him welcome, and he taught them how to dance and sing.

One day, a huge storm blew up. Two boys ran into the serpent's hut looking for shelter, but the serpent was hungry and swallowed them whole.

Next day, he secretly left the village. When the people found that the boys were missing, they gave chase.

They found the serpent fast asleep, coiled around a mountain. Silently, they crept closer and cut a slit in his side. But the two boys had turned into parrots and they flew away.

Then the Rainbow Serpent woke up. Furious to find a gash in his side, he coiled tighter and tighter, until the mountain shattered and rocks fell across the countryside. A storm raged across the sky and rain poured down. Then he slithered off underground, leaving hills, lakes and rivers behind.

3-second sum-up

The Rainbow Serpent came to Earth, creating hills, rivers, lakes and rain

Dreamtime

In Aboriginal belief, all the features of the Earth are sacred. They were created by the ancestor spirits long ago, in a time called the Dreamtime. The ancestor spirits travelled across Australia, some as humans, some as animals, shaping the landscape as they went.

The gourd children

...in 30 seconds (Chinese)

One summer's day, a farmer was working in his fields when he heard a rumble of thunder. Quickly, he sent his children inside and hung an iron cage from the door. Soon, a storm was raging and down from the clouds flew the thunder god. The farmer pushed the thunder god into the cage and slammed the door shut.

The farmer wanted to teach the thunder god a lesson. He planned to kill him, then pickle him.

Next day, the farmer went to market. He told his children not to give the thunder god anything to drink. But the thunder god begged and pleaded until the children granted his wish. At once, he burst out of his cage. He gave the children a tooth and told them to plant it in the ground, where it sprouted and grew a large gourd.

Then the thunder god left. Almost at once, the rain began to fall so hard that the Earth was flooded and everyone drowned except for the children, who survived by floating safely away in their gourd.

3-second sum-up

A farmer trapped the thunder god, who sent a flood as punishment

Flood myths

Most of the world's cultures have myths or stories about tremendous floods that destroy the Earth and drown nearly everyone. Usually, the gods or spirits send the floods as a punishment for people's wickedness. After the flood, a new and better world appears.

Creatures and monsters

Strange creatures and fabulous beasts roar, rage and stomp through many myths from around the world. Pitted against them are heroes and gods who hunt down and kill the creatures to stop them causing more evil and harm. In this chapter, there are tales of a beast with a bull-head that lived in a maze, a monster that munchedthe clouds and turned people to stone, a serpent that goaded the gods, a fire-breathing dragon . . . and a dragon-slayer.

Creatures and monsters
Glossary

Aegir (ay-ir) In Norse myths, the god of the sea and the brewer of beer for the gods.

Ahaiyuta (a-hi-yuta) In Native American myths, a boy who killed the monstrous **Cloud Eater**.

Ariadne In Greek myths, a princess who helped **Theseus** to kill the **Minotaur**. Later, Theseus abandoned her.

Cloud Eater In Native American myths, a terrible monster that ate the clouds so that the rain could not fall.

Fafnir In Norse myths, a human who stole a hoard of cursed gold from his father, **Hreidmar** He turned himself into a dragon and was killed by his nephew, **Sigurd**.

gopher A small burrowing animal, similar to a squirrel.

foretold The past tense of foretell – to say what will happen in the future, using magic powers.

Gorgon In Greek myths, one of three hideous sisters who had once been beautiful women. The Gorgons' glance turned people to stone.

Hreidmar (h-rade-mar) In Norse myths, a magician and the father of **Fafnir**. He owned a hoard of cursed gold.

Hymir (he-mir) In Norse myths, a giant who owned a huge cauldron wanted by **Aegir** for brewing beer. He took **Thor** on a dangerous fishing trip.

Jormungand (yor-mun-gand) In Norse myths, a gigantic, poisonous sea serpent that circled the world.

Medusa In Greek myths, a **Gorgon**. She had snakes for hair and could turn people to stone with a look.

Minotaur In Greek myths, a monster with the head of a bull and the body of a man. It lived in a labryinth (a type of maze) on the island of Crete.

nymph In Greek myths, a nature spirit in the form of a young woman.

Perseus In Greek myths, a hero sent to kill **Medusa**, a **Gorgon**.

Regin In Norse myths, a human and the brother of **Fafnir**. He was killed by his nephew, **Sigurd**.

Sigurd In Norse myths, a human and nephew of **Regin** and **Fafnir**. Sigurd killed them both and took Fafnir's stolen gold.

Theseus In Greek myths, a hero who sailed to Crete and killed the **Minotaur** with the help of **Ariadne**.

Theseus and the Minotaur

...in 30 seconds (Greek)

On the island of Crete, King Minos kept a terrible, bull-headed creature, called the Minotaur, in a maze-like labyrinth. Every nine years, he demanded that 14 young people be sent from Athens to be fed to the beast.

One year, Theseus, son of the king of Athens, volunteered to try to kill the monster even though no one had ever come out of the labyrinth alive.

When Theseus arrived on Crete, the king's daughter, Ariadne, fell in love with him and offered to help him if he married her. She gave him a magic ball of string.

Theseus tied one end to the entrance of the labyrinth, and unwound the string as he went. Inside the maze, he put the Minotaur to death. Then he followed the string safely out again. Taking Ariadne and his fellow Athenians with him, Theseus sailed for home. But he forgot his promise to marry Ariadne. He left her on the island of Naxos and was later punished by the gods.

3-second sum-up

Theseus killed the Minotaur that had caused terror on Crete

3-minute quest
Design a monster

Myths are full of people-eating monsters. Some have many heads, huge, sharp claws or are part-animal, part-human.

Design your own mythical beast using different parts from the monsters in this book. Give your monster a terrifying name.

Sigurd slays the dragon

...in 30 seconds (Norse)

Long ago, a magician's son, Fafnir, killed his father, Hreidmar, and stole his hoard of gold. The gold had been given to Hreidmar by the gods and it was cursed to bring misery and death to whoever owned it. This evil curse drove Fafnir to turn himself into a dragon to guard his ill-gotten treasure.

Meanwhile, Fafnir's brother, Regin, brought up their nephew, Sigurd, to avenge Hreidmar's death and win back the gold.

Armed with a powerful sword forged by Regin, Sigurd set off. When he was near Fafnir's lair, he hid until the dragon came out for a drink. Quick as a flash, Sigurd drew out his sword and killed it. Then he roasted and ate the dragon's heart.

Tasting the heart gave Sigurd the power to understand the language of the birds. They warned him that Regin was planning to kill him and seize the gold. So Sigurd killed Regin and saved himself.

3-second sum-up

Sigurd killed a dragon to win back his grandfather's stolen gold

St George

Many myths feature dragon slayers. St George is one of the most famous. He was a knight in the Middle East who hunted down a ferocious dragon that was terrorizing a town. It had eaten all the young girls and was about to devour the king's daughter. After a terrible fight, St George killed it and rescued the princess.

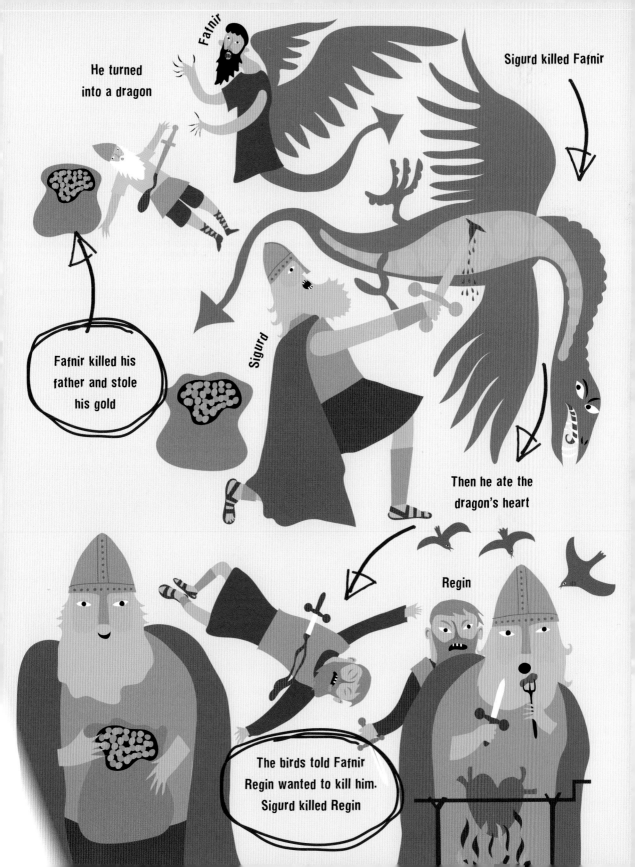

Ahaiyuta and the Cloud Eater
...in 30 seconds (Native American)

The Cloud Eater, a dreadful monster, lived on a great mountain. Each morning, he stood on the mountain top, and gobbled down every single cloud. Without clouds, the rain stopped falling and soon the land was struck by a terrible drought. The crops died and people went hungry. Many brave warriors tried to track down and kill the Cloud Eater but none succeeded.

A boy called Ahaiyuta decided to try his luck. His grandmother gave him four magic feathers: red, blue, yellow and black.

Ahaiyuta stuck the red feather in his hair. It guided him along the right path, where he met a gopher. Ahaiyuta used the yellow feather to shrink down to the gopher's size; the blue feather allowed him to talk its language. The gopher led Ahaiyuta into its burrow and along a tunnel that led to the Cloud Eater's home. Ahaiyuta put the black feather in his hair. It gave him the power to kill the monster, bringing back clouds and rain to the world.

3-second sum-up

With the help of magic feathers, Ahaiyuta killed the Cloud Eater

3-minute quest WANTED!

Design a Wild West-style 'Wanted!' poster calling for all brave warriors to track down the Cloud Eater. Include:

- A picture and description of him.
- A list of his deadliest features and his worst crimes.
- A reward for his capture.

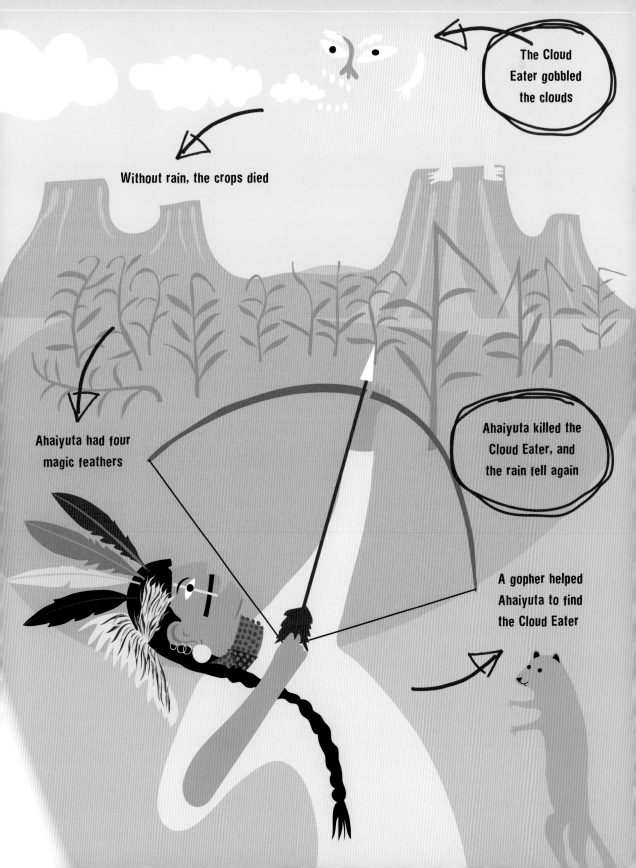

Perseus and Medusa

...in 30 seconds (Greek)

Perseus and his mother, Danae, were cast adrift at sea by his grandfather, who feared that Perseus would kill him. They floated to the island of Seriphos and were rescued by King Polydectes.

One day, the king invited Perseus to a banquet and told him to bring a horse as a gift. Perseus did not have a horse so he asked the king to suggest another gift.

The king told him to bring back the head of the terrible Gorgon, Medusa, whose glance turned people to stone.

Perseus asked the gods for help. They gave him winged sandals, a sharp sickle, a shiny shield and a helmet that made him invisible. When Perseus found Medusa, he flew above her and raised his shield and sickle. Then, looking at her reflection in his shield, he cut off her head with his sickle and put it in a bag.

Back on Seriphos, Polydectes was forcing Danae to marry him. Perseus pulled Medusa's head from the bag and held it up – the king instantly turned to stone.

3-second sum-up

Using magic gifts from the gods, Perseus killed Medusa the Gorgon

Who was Medusa?

Medusa was one of three monstrous sisters called the Gorgons. She had once been a beautiful nymph. One day she badly offended the goddess, Athene, who turned her flowing hair into wriggling, poisonous snakes, and made her lovely face hideously ugly.

Thor goes fishing

...in 30 seconds (Norse)

Once, Aegir, the sea god, brewed some ale for the other gods but did not have a pot big enough to hold it. Thor knew that the giant, Hymir, owned a huge cauldron and offered to fetch it. Thor stayed overnight in Hymir's hall and enjoyed a huge feast.

Next morning, the giant set out on a fishing trip and Thor begged to go with him. The two of them rowed further and further out to sea, each determined to outdo the other.

Soon, Hymir caught two huge whales. Not to be beaten, Thor baited his own line with an ox's head and cast it overboard. At once, he got a catch.

The gigantic sea serpent, Jormungand, had snatched the bait. It thrashed and writhed as the hook caught fast in its throat. Fist over fist, Thor hauled in his line until he was close enough to bring his hammer down on the serpent's head. He cut the line, and with a roar, the serpent sank to the bottom of the sea.

3-second sum-up

Thor went fishing with the giant, Hymir, and hooked the monstrous serpent, Jormungand

Who was Jormungand?

Jormungand was a gigantic serpent and the enemy of the gods. Odin, the chief god, hurled him out of Asgard (heaven) into the ocean, where he grew so big that he could circle the Earth and catch his own tail. It was foretold that Thor would kill him one day, but would die from Jormungand's poison.

Discover more

FICTION BOOKS

The Heroes of Olympus series by Rick Riordan
Puffin Books, from 2010

Percy Jackson and the Olympians series by Rick Riordan
Puffin Books, 2005–09

Legends series by Anthony Horowitz
Kingfisher, 2012

NON-FICTION BOOKS

African Myths and Legends by Catherine Chambers
Raintree, 2013

American Indian Myths and Legends by Catherine Chambers
Raintree, 2013

The Children's Book of Myths and Legends
by Ronne Randall and Graham Howell
Armadillo Books, 2011

Greek Myths by Marcia Williams
Walker Books, 2006

Norse Myths and Legends by Anita Ganeri
Raintree, 2013

The Orchard Book of Aesop's Fables by Michael Morpurgo
Orchard, 2004

Roman Myths by Kathy Elgin and Fiona Sansom
Franklin Watts, 2012

Usborne Book of Greek Myths by Anna Milbourne and Louie Stowell
Usborne, 2010

World Myths and Legends by Kathryn Ceceri
Nomad Press, 2010

DVDs – suitable for all ages

Joseph Campbell – The Power of Myth, with Bill Moyers.
The PBS series on world mythology **Acorn, 2011**

Irish Myths and Legends **Delta, 2003**

Kirikou and the Sorceress **BFI, 2003**

Myths and Legends: Robin Hood/Camelot **Abbey, 2008**

The Storyteller: Greek Myths **Sony Pictures, 1990**

WEBSITES

African folk tales
http://ccs.clarityconnect.com/NRiggs/AfricanFolktales.html
Stories from several African countries

Ancient Chinese stories
http://china.mrdonn.org/stories.html
Myths and information about Chinese history

Children's Native American stories
http://www.apples4theteacher.com/native-american/short-stories/
A series of traditional tales

Greek mythology for kids
http://greece.mrdonn.org/myths.html
Many stories and information about gods and goddesses

Kids Web Japan
http://web-japan.org/kidsweb/folk/index.html
A huge selection of legends from Japan,
told with pictures

Myths about gods of ancient cultures
http://gwydir.demon.co.uk/jo/myths.htm
Website for 7–11 year olds about
Roman, Egyptian and Norse gods.

Index

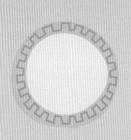